uthor

NOWN

URDES

By the same A

MAN THE UNK

PRAYER

VOYAGE TO LO